I AM A VERY RICH MAN...

...EVEN THOUGH, GENERATIONS AGO, THE FIRST GLOBAL TYRANT LAID DOWN CERTAIN RESTRICTIONS AGAINST MY KIND EVER OWNING PROPERTY.

BUT THE WORLD WAS A DIFFERENT PLACE THEN. ONE OF THE TYRANT'S TEPID DESCENDANTS NOW SITS IN HIS STEAD.

HEH.

D1199484

IMITATION OF LIFE

SO FUCK ALL THAT OTHER SHIT.

Ah, YES. *WELLLL* ... IT PROBABLY WON'T SURPRISE YOU TO LEARN THAT MINISTER RAIKSHAW IS PART OF A CONTINGENT THAT IS ... SHALL WE SAY, *LESS* THAN PLEASED WITH THE CURRENT IMPERIAL LEADERSHIP.

DRINK?

THE GRENDEL-KHAN'S AN ABSOLUTE SHIT-FOR-BRAINS. THAT'S NO NEWS. AND, YES, WE'VE KNOWN ABOUT THIS *"SECRET"* SOCIETY FOR MONTHS NOW.

I CAN *SMELL* THAT GUN, DICKHEAD. LUCKY FOR YOU, IT'S *UNLOADED.*

Heh, Heh, Heh...

CALM YOURSELF, BLUE. MY MANSERVANT WAS MERELY OFFERING YOU A GLASS OF POMEGRANATE WINE.

Eh? Oh.

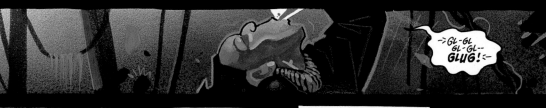

->GL-GL GL-GL-- *GLUG!*<-

A CLONE'S *APPETITE* ... ENOUGH TO RIVAL MY OWN! ANYWAY, MINISTER RAIKSHAW BORE NEWS OF A CLANDESTINE MISSION THE KHAN HAS JUST BEGUN.

FOR WHICH HE HAS CHARTERED THE TALENTS OF THE *SESSION* TWINS.

THE *SESSIONS*?!

Hmm... HE'S MORE *DESPERATE* THAN WE SUSPECTED.

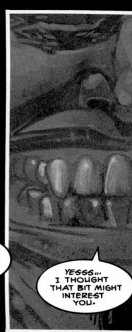

YESSS... I THOUGHT THAT BIT MIGHT INTEREST YOU.

THEN YOU SHOULD KNOW THAT MY BROTHERS AND I HAVE NO DESIRE TO MIX IT UP WITH *THOSE* CRAZY BITCHES. I'M GOING TO HAVE TO *PASS* ON THIS ONE.

THANK YOU FO THE UNPOISONE WINE.

HE'S SENT THEM TO SEARCH FOR THE MAN-MACHINE, *GRENDEL-PRIME.*

CUTE.

WELL, I HOPE YOU ENJOYED THAT LITTLE DISPLAY. IT'S GOING TO COST YOU TEN THOUSAND.

A BARGAIN.

AND NO MORE TRICKS LIKE THAT. IF YOU WANT US TO PULL THIS EXCURSION OFF, WE'LL HAVE NO TIME FOR YOUR PETTY ENTERTAINMENTS.

I WOULDN'T HAVE IT ANY OTHER WAY.

FUCK YOU.

WELL, THAT CERTAINLY WAS EXHILARATING. ORDER US A NEW JAGUAR AND SEND MY REGARDS TO MARTIN RAIKSHAW'S WIDOW.

Y-YUP.

CHG··CHG··CHG··CHG··CHG··CHG

:PANT: :PANT: :PANT:

:PANT: :PANT:

MINING COMPANY THOUGHT THIS VEIN WAS EXHAUSTED. THEY WERE WRONG.

KRANG

TAK

SSSSSSS

:GASP:

N-GHUHH...

I HAVEN'T FOUND ENOUGH HERE TO FINANCE THE PROCEDURE YET, BABY.

BUT I KNOW THAT MOTHER LODE'S DOWN THERE, DARLIN'.

AND I'M NOT GIVING UP ON US.

AFTER YOU LEFT, I DID SOME... HORRIBLE THINGS FOR MONEY. FINALLY SAVED UP ENOUGH FOR A COUPLE OF WIND TURBINES...

...THAT CLUNKY OLD EXCAVATION SUIT, AND THE CLAIM TO THIS DIG.

ZZZZZZEEEEEEEEEEEEEEEE

COMPANY'S LEFTOVER WATER PUMP STILL WORKS FINE.

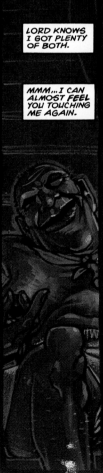

NOW IT'S ONLY A MATTER OF TIME, DARLIN'.

TIME AND DESIRE.

LORD KNOWS I GOT PLENTY OF BOTH.

MMM... I CAN ALMOST FEEL YOU TOUCHING ME AGAIN.

THAT WAY YOU USED TO TICKLE... EH?!

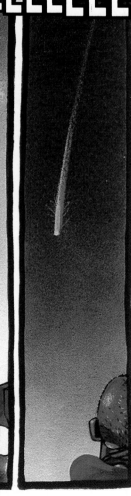

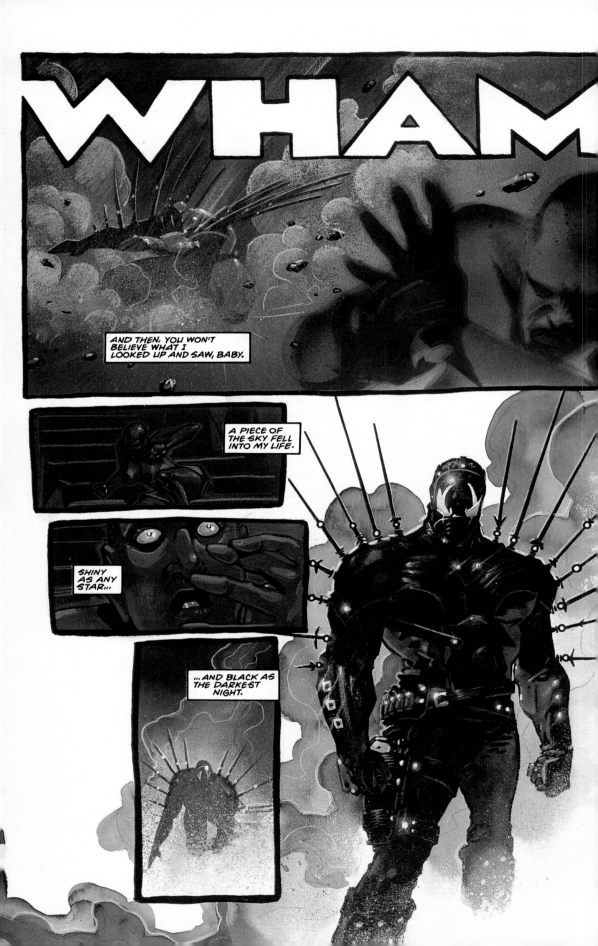

JUST LIKE YOU SAID.

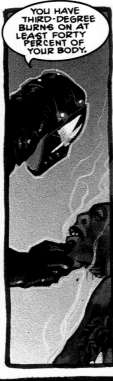

YOU HAVE THIRD-DEGREE BURNS ON AT LEAST FORTY PERCENT OF YOUR BODY.

WITHOUT A RADIO, I CANNOT SUMMON AID -- AND I CANNOT RISK DETECTION IN THIS AREA. I TRULY REGRET THIS SITUATION.

BUT YOU SHOULD HAVE HEEDED MY WARNING.

AND THEN IT WAS OVER, JUST LIKE THAT.

FUT!

I DON'T BEAR A GRUDGE THOUGH, REALLY. THIS WAS ALWAYS A LONG SHOT, AFTER ALL.

AND WE ARE TOGETHER NOW. SORT OF.

SHACT

STILL, I DO BEAR A TON OF REGRETS.

REGRETS THAT THE WORLD DOESN'T TREAT ITS LOVERS BETTER. REGRETS THAT I NEVER COULD AFFORD THE PROCEDURE FOR YOUR NEW BODY.

BUT MOST OF ALL...

...I REGRET THAT I DIDN'T TURN YOU AROUND TO FACE THE SUNSET THAT DAY, DARLIN'.

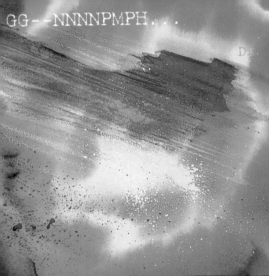

LABOR PAINS.

WAS IN AWE----NO! NO! I'M BEGGING YOU! *PLEEEEAAAAAA*

OH, MY GOD, MICHAEL! Y--you . . .

I--I...yes, I understand.
Of course. Privacy

Michael! What was that all about?
Was that...was that really   HI

My GOD, Michael,
do you think it's a good idea to get involved in thi

Mr. Creach, you ARE my business.
He's a fucking machine, after all!
A killing machine

I don't trust...it.

I...I don't--Michael? Pleassse--

C'MON! C'MON!

OKAY, MAGGIE, THIS ONE'S COMING AROUND AGAIN.

FAP! FAP! FAP!

HE'S ALL YOURS.

OBSERVE. YOUR SCALP.

A SMALL PIECE OF FLESH. EASILY REPLACED. UNLIKE SO MANY OTHERS.

ICHAEL, PLEEEEEASE...

I -- I don't know what to say to convince you!

s is sheer insanity--
the whims of an inhuman fiend.

I--I know.

he perfect subject...if anyone could withstand the strain--

ichael, please, I love you.
I'm just worried about

JEALOUS?!

F A FUCKING PILE OF CIRCUITS?!

Dr. Creach? Dr. Creach? Your visitor is here again.

Natasha, the doctor is very busy today...the lab can wait.

Michael, this madness has to end.
You never sleep, hardly eat...Michael, it's dangerous!

You've locked me out of the lab--
and yourself out of the bedroo

Michael, you're
becoming like HIM!!

at least tell me what it is that

Dr. Creach,
there's a transmission from the science council.
They want to know

No, you tell them!

If you insist on cutting me out of your life, then I won't

Michael, please, I'm sorry...
I'm just...Michael.

THESE DAYS, THERE ARE MANY NAMES FOR MY KIND: SPY, OPERATIVE, TERRORIST, ASSASSIN, GRENDEL.

I PREFER JUST "THIEF." SIMPLE AND DIRECT.

NO MATTER HOW ELSE THEY THINK OF IT, PEOPLE HIRE ME TO STEAL THINGS: DOCUMENTS, CIRCUITS, SECRETS, LIVES.

RIGSVILE

IN THIS CASE, IT'S MOST OF THE ABOVE.

SN'RRRRKT

MY BROTHER, RED, HAS JUST SET ME DOWN IN THE GOBI DESERT; THIS IS AS FAR AS A TRANSPORT CAN SAFELY VENTURE.

FROM HERE, I'M ON MY OWN.

I MUST COVER NEARLY SEVENTY MILES ON FOOT BY NIGHTFALL.

A PLEASANT IDLE.

THE DESERT'S A GODDAMN HOLIDAY FOR ME: SMOOTH, AUSTERE...

... QUIET...

... AND, MOST IMPORTANTLY...

... WARM.

Ahhhh...

WUMP.!

AT TWENTY-THREE MINUTES TILL SUNDOWN, I ARRIVE AT THE FOOTHILLS.

A RING OF SECURITY DEVICES ENCIRCLES THE VALLEY OF SHIT. MAKES AN AIR-STRIKE NEARLY IMPOSSIBLE.

BESIDES, I HAVE NO CAUSE TO DESTROY THIS SQUALID PIT.

ONLY A PORTION OF ITS RESIDENTS.

THE SECURITY ON THE GROUND IS NIL -- THE MESSAGE CLEAR. IF YOU WISH TO ENTER THIS TOILET TOWN...

...FEEL FREE.

le STY

YOU'RE ON YOUR OWN.

THERE ARE ONE HUNDRED AND TWENTY-THREE PERSONS ON THE GROUND LEVEL OF THIS BUILDING.

MOST ARE ARMED, AND ALL ARE INTOXICATED.

EASIER, EVEN, THAN I HAD THOUGHT.

UNH...?

NEON BLITZ, PLEASE. STRAIGHT UP.

HERE IT COMES--

HEY, BLUE BOY...

--THREE HUNDRED POUNDS OF ASSHOLE.

Huh, Huh...

YER BALLS'R'BLUE, TOO, I'LL BET. AN' YER LITTLE WEENIE, TOO! Huh, Huh...

THIS IS IT. A GOOD OPPORTUNITY.

MANY EYES ARE WATCHING THIS BRUTAL FARCE.

H--

THIS ONE'S LIGHTLY ARMED: RAZOR IN POCKET, GUN IN BOOT, SHRAPNEL IN BRAIN.

TALL ONE'S GOT A BARBED-WIRE CHAIN.

BALD ONE'S A TOUGH GUY.

HRRMPH.

STUPID, PATHETIC FUCKS.

NOTHING BUT PILES OF WASTED FLESH:

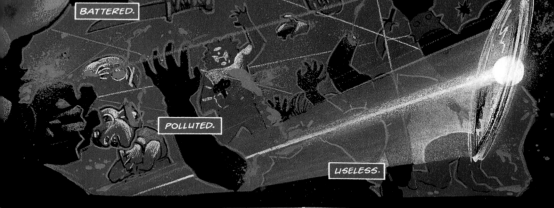

BATTERED.

POLLUTED.

USELESS.

THEY THINK

THEY'VE SEEN

EVERYTHING.

NOT ONE DESERVES A GRENDEL'S DEATH.

DON'T *PISS ME* OFF!

OKAY, MAN, OKAY...

"... YOU MADE YER POINT. WHAT IS IT, THEN?"

I WANT TO SEE *VASELINE TSUSUMI*.

ACCOMPANIED BY A PAIR OF EDGY GOONS.

BOTH UNARMED.

HIDDEN LASERS FOCUSED ON MY EVERY MOVE.

I EVEN GET TO SEE THE BIG MAN ALONE.

ENGAGED, EVEN.

SOON I'M HEADING DOWN AN ELEVATOR.

YES, O WAYWARD GRENDEL?

I HEAR YOU WISH TO SPEAK WITH ME?

THIS MAN... THIS SWOLLEN CYST OF FLESH RECENTLY SOLD SLAVES TO GRENDEL-PRIME. A RARE PERSONAL ENCOUNTER.

I HAVE NO DOUBT THAT I CAN PURCHASE ALL THE INFORMATION ABOUT THIS MEETING THAT I DESIRE.

THESE POWER-FUCKS ARE THE SAME ALL AROUND THE WORLD. EVERYTHING'S FOR SALE IN THE END.

IT'S GETTING A GODDAMN APPOINTMENT THAT'S SO HARD!

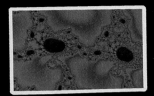

AS A DOCTOR, I UNDERSTAND THAT LITTLE OF WHAT WE PERCEIVE IS CONSTANT.

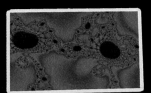

EVEN EQUATIONAL SCIENCE IS GIVEN TO DISTORTION.

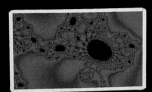

MEAT MACHINE

IT HAS LONG BEEN A PASSION OF MINE TO CONNECT SOMEDAY WITH THE SOURCE OF THESE IRREGULARITIES.

TO THE WORLD AT LARGE, MY THEORIES ARE OBSCENE.

EVEN BEFORE THE CYBORG-WARRIOR ENLISTED MY AID, THE DIRECTIONS OF MY RESEARCH WERE THUS: TO CAPTURE AND HARNESS THE SPARK OF NEUROLOGICAL ENERGY RELEASED AT DEATH.

A BURST THAT I HAVE TERMED THE NECRONOVA.

WHEN THIS ELUSIVE AND POWERFUL FORCE IS PROPERLY FOCUSED, THE EQUATIONS DISTORT...

...PERCEPTIONS EXPAND...

...AND REALITY TREMBLES.

DR. CREACH.

I HAVE MORE FODDER.

THE ONLY DRAWBACK TO THIS DARING PREMISE IS THE SHEER VOLUME OF RAW MATERIALS REQUIRED. THUS, FOR REASONS OF SECRECY, OUR SELECTION FROM THE VARIOUS SLAVE TRADERS WAS LIMITED.

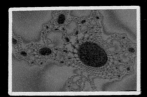 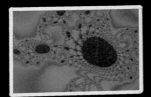 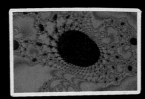

MAINLY THE AGED AND INFIRM.

ONE IN THE SOUTH-EAST TERMINAL AND ONE IN THE NORTH-WEST.

QUICKLY!

GOOD! THE RIP IS BEGINNING TO ENLARGE.

STILL, WE HAVE FED SOME TWO THOUSAND SOULS INTO THE MACHINE.

NOT ENOUGH.

WELL?

PATIENCE!

THE MACHINE REQUIRES SEVERAL MOMENTS TO PROCESS THE ENERGY.

HRRMMM...

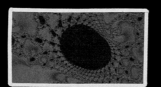

THE EQUATIONS DISTORT.

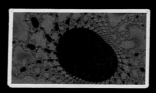

PERCEPTIONS EXPAND.

REALITY TREMBLES.

THE POSITION IS SLIPPING! WE NEED MORE FUEL!

THE YOUNGEST YOU CAN FIND!

WE'RE IN.

SURELY, THE TASK WASN'T EASY OR BRIEF. THE CRITERIA WERE BOTH ARCANE AND PRECISE:

FRAGMENTS OF THE *TRUE SKULL* AS WELL AS THIS BUNKER'S LOCALE...

... DEEP BENEATH THE DEVIL'S ORIGINAL HOME...

...ALL COMBINED TO GIVE FOCUS TO OUR PURSUIT.

TO GO BEYOND EXISTENCE AND PHYSICS.

TO MAKE REALITY TREMBLE AND TWIST.

TO LET THE HUNTER ARISE!

WELL, WELL, SISTER...

PRETTY LIGHTS. SILLY MEN.

YES!

YES! I SEE IT! AT LAST!

THE ESSENCE... THE SPIRIT... THE *SOUL* OF HUNTER ROSE!

FUCK 'EM UP!

BLAM!

Total Systems Failure

Emergency Generators engaged

N-N-NO... WH-WHA-- DID...

SISTER?

ASSESSMENT.

UNSURE. KEEP YOUR GUARD UP.

HE'S GONE!

B-BUT... H-HOW COULD THAT BE? THIS WAS A COMMUNICATION PORTAL, NOT A TRANSPORT DEVICE. HOW COULD HE --?

THERE'S NOT EVEN A TRACE OF RESIDUE.

HOW?

WHERE IS HE, SHITFACE?!

HOLD HIM HERE. I'LL SCOUT AROUND A BIT. WE'LL GET SOME ANSWERS.

Oh, YESSS...

NMMPH!

YOU! YOU...

...FUCKING BITCHES! WHAT DID YOU DO TO THE GR--

--URK!

3/14/07 -- THE KHAN WAS UNABLE TO SLEEP FOR MORE THAN SIXTEEN MINUTES.

PACING BEGAN AT · 7:23 P.M. AND CONTINUED THROUGHOUT THE NIGHT.

HABITUAL FACIAL SCRATCHING BEGAN SHORTLY THEREAFTER, DESPITE AVERSION THERAPY.

TO QUOTE A 22ND-CENTURY POET: "AND BLEATING WITH AN INELOQUENT GRACE."

I WAS SUMMONED SHORTLY AFTER MIDNIGHT.

BABYLON · CRASH ·

LAWYER SEM-165 --
LOGGED 12:15 A.M.

EXCELLENCY?

WHAT CAN I ACCOMPLISH FOR YOU TODAY?

WELL?

DID YOU HEAR THE LATEST REPORTS? THOSE FLICKING CLAN-SLAMMERS DOWN SOLITH HAVE DECLARED ALITONOMY!

FLICKING DECLARED IT!

SECTION 19, PARAGRAPH 8 OF THE BRAXILIAN CHARTER CONFIRMS THEIR RIGHT TO MAKE SUCH A CLAIM. INTERIOR SUPPORT OF LOCAL INDUSTRY HAS BEEN --

WELL, WE JUST DON'T HAVE THE FLICKING MONEY!

CIGARETTE.

THESE GODDAMN PROVINCIALS -- THEY... THEY ALL WANT TO BE THE FLICKING EMPIRE!

HISTORICAL UPRISINGS OF THIS SORT ARE COMMON. PAST GRENDEL-KHANS HAVE ALWAYS MANAGED TO --

SPARE ME. WHAT ABOUT CHINA?

THE MANDARIN CLAN YESTERDAY ORDERED A BAN ON ALL GATHERINGS OF MORE THAN THREE GRENDELS AT A TIME.

SO FAR, SEVENTEEN EXECUTIONS HAVE RESULTED.

CORRECTION: NINETEEN.

FLICKING YELLOW BASTARDS. THEY THINK THIS IS EASY?! THEY THINK THEY COULD DO BETTER?

LIGHT.

FUCK ME.

Ah -- →HUGK← →HUGK← →HUGK← →HUGK← →HUGK← →HUGK←

THE IMPERIAL PHYSICIAN HAS ADVISED AGAINST THE USE OF HEROIN CIG--

SH-- →HUGK← →HUGK←

-- SHUT THE FUCK UP.

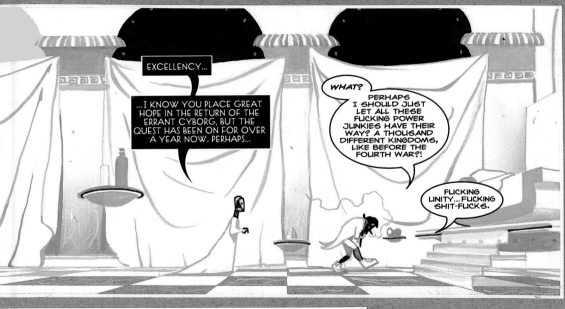

EXCELLENCY...

...I KNOW YOU PLACE GREAT HOPE IN THE RETURN OF THE ERRANT CYBORG, BUT THE QUEST HAS BEEN ON FOR OVER A YEAR NOW. PERHAPS...

WHAT?

PERHAPS I SHOULD JUST LET ALL THESE FUCKING POWER JUNKIES HAVE THEIR WAY? A THOUSAND DIFFERENT KINGDOMS, LIKE BEFORE THE FOURTH WAR?!

FUCKING UNITY...FUCKING SHIT-FUCKS.

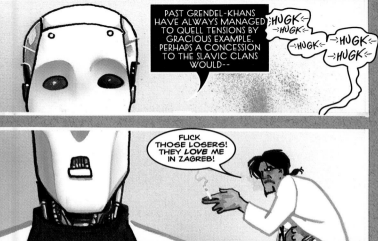

PAST GRENDEL-KHANS HAVE ALWAYS MANAGED TO QUELL TENSIONS BY GRACIOUS EXAMPLE. PERHAPS A CONCESSION TO THE SLAVIC CLANS WOULD--

→HUGK← →HUGK← →HUGK← →HUGK← →HUGK← →HUGK←

FUCK THOSE LOSERS! THEY *LOVE* ME IN ZAGREB!

FUCKING LOVE ME...

HOLO-VID... ON.

...DEMANDS MADE BY THE SOUTHERN CLANS CENTER ON THE ISSUE OF INCREASED IMPERIAL SUBSIDIES. AS BRAXILIAN FORCES MOVE NORTHWARD...

...CLAN LEADERS SAY THEY STILL HAVE HOPES FOR A RECONCILIATION.

HEAR THAT? FLICKING SPICS STILL WANT TO CLI A DEAL! I TOLD Y--

PERHAPS.

WE NOW TAKE YOU, LIVE, TO THE SIEGE OF MEXICO CITY -- ALREADY IN PROGRESS.

FLICK.

I ALWAYS LIKED MEXICO CITY...

EXCELLENCY. I'M RECEIVING A TRANSMISSION LINKUP DIRECT FROM MARGARET SESSION...

THE SESSIONS?! WELL, FUCK, PUT IT ON! PUT IT--

TRANSFERRING TO ON-SCREEN.

GREETINGS, GRENDEL-KHAN.

I BRING YOU NEWS OF OUR CONTINUING QUEST FOR THE--

YES, YES! WHAT NEWS?! WHAT NEWS?!

I REGRET TO INFORM YOU THAT THE BEING KNOWN AS GRENDEL-PRIME HAS BEEN DESTROYED.

F-- HOW?!--

MY SISTER AND I TRAILED HIS ACTIVITIES TO THE MANHATTAN WASTES. THERE, AN EXPERIMENT OF HIS OWN DEVISING SEEMS TO HAVE ERADICATED HIM.

BUT-- BUT... ARE YOU SURE?! IT COULD BE SOME SORT OF RUSE!

IT COULD B--

WE WITNESSED THE ACCIDENT.

BUT...

WE HAVE THEREFORE DECIDED TO SETTLE FOR A REDUCED FEE. TWO BILLION.

AS ALWAYS, GREAT KHAN...

...IT HAS BEEN OUR EXTREME PLEASURE SERVICING YOU.

BUT...

VIVAT GRENDEL.

OFUCK!

DESTROYED?! BUT... BUT HOW?! THAT FUCKING BASTARD WAS BUILT TO LAST FOREVER! WHAT WAS HE DOING?!

THOSE FUCKING CRYPTIC BITCHES! TWO BILLION! OFUCK-OFUCK-OFUCK...

URINAL!

URINAL!

DESTROYED... IT JUST DOESN'T MAKE SENSE...

WITH THIS LATEST BIT OF INTELLIGENCE, YOUR POLITICAL OPTIONS HAVE BEEN NEUTERED.

MAYBE HE WAS TRYING TO-- HUH?!

THE RELOCATION OF THE GRENDEL-PRIME WAS YOUR FINAL HOPE OF SECURING THE LOYALTIES OF THE INTERNATIONAL COMMUNITY -- A CHANCE TO RECLAIM SOME OF YOUR GREAT-GRANDFATHER'S GLORY.

NOW, WAIT A MINUTE...

YOUR ONLY RECOURSE NOW IS TO GIVE IN TO THE DEMANDS FOR CLAN AUTONOMY -- TO FRACTURE THE EMPIRE INTO FIEFDOMS.

NO! WAIT, SEM-165! THIS ISN'T OVER YET! WE CAN STILL--

THIS BEING THE CASE, A PROTOCOL LAWYER WILL BETTER SUIT YOUR NEEDS.

WAIT-- OOMPH!

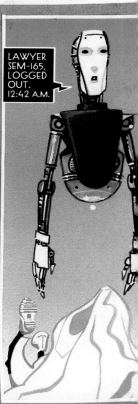

LAWYER SEM-165, LOGGED OUT. 12:42 A.M.

OH, YEAH?! WELL, JUST *FUCK YOU*, 165! FUCK YOU! FUCK YOU! FUCK YOU!

FUCKING DICKLESS PILE OF CIRCUITS! FUCKING LAWYERS! THINK YOU GOT IT ALL FUCKING FIGURED OUT!

-: Pant - Pant :-

SHIT. HE'S GOT TO BE WRONG! THERE'S GOT TO BE A WAY OUT OF THIS TRAP.

GOT TO.

LET'S SEE. THERE'S ALWAYS AFRICA. STILL LOYAL.

MAYBE ANOTHER IMPERIAL EDICT. FUCK.

ONE DAY EVERYONE WANTS TO EAT YOUR SHIT.

THE NEXT DAY THEY WANT TO EAT YOUR GUTS.

THE NEXT DAY THEY WANT TO EAT YOUR BRAINS.

I KNOW. I'LL SEND THE IMPERIAL GUARD SOUTH.

WELL, I HATE TO TELL YOU ASSHOLES, IT SUCKS.

FUCK, FUCK, SHIT, FUCK, BASTARD, CLINT.

FUCK, I—I CAN'T LOSE ALL THIS. I CAN'T!

TO THE BORDER. SET UP A DEMOLITION BARRIER.

SONSABITCHES! THEY ALL WANNA BE BIG DOG.

IT'S ALL I'VE EVER KNOWN. ALL I'VE EVER BEEN.

FUCK, FUCK, SHIT, FUCK, BASTARD, CLINT, SHIT.

WASTE THOSE FUCKIN' SPICS. NAH. OBVIOUS.

BUT... THAT WAS YEARS AGO. FUCK. FUCK. FUCK.

FUCK, THEY USED TO STAND IN LINE FOR THOSE.

I KNOW! I'LL SELL SOME MORE IMPERIAL FAVORS.

I MET A BLUE MAN THE OTHER DAY.

WE SHARED AN ENERGY SPHERE ON ONE OF THE MIDDLE STEPPES.

HIS LAST, HE CLAIMED.

HE SAID IT WAS TIME TO GO HOME.

THIS WAS WELL.

HIS PRESENCE DISTURBED THE LOCAL SHERPAS.

IN THE DEPTHS OF HIS UNNATURAL EYES, I COULD SEE DEATH AFTER DEATH AFTER DEATH. A CONTAGION OF RAGE AND DESPAIR.

AS I CAUTIOUSLY LISTENED, HE SPOKE OF A QUEST GONE AWRY.

I HAVE SEARCHED FOR THE ESSENCE OF GRENDEL AND FOUND NOTHING -- NOTHING BUT AVARICE AND SELF-PITY.

MY OPPONENTS HAVE ABANDONED THE QUEST. MY PATRON HAS RENEGED ON OUR CONTRACT.

THE KHAN IS NOW DEAD, OF HIS OWN INDOLENT HAND.

NOTHING INHABITS MY THOUGHTS, AND OBLIVION DRIVES MY DESIRES.

EVENTUALLY, THE BLUE MAN REVEALED THE SOURCE OF HIS FRUSTRATION -- A CAMPAIGN TO UNVEIL THE EXILE OF A LEGEND. I DIDN'T TELL HIM SO, BUT I KNEW A MAN WHO HAD SEEN THE GRENDEL-PRIME. HE DIDN'T LIKE TO SPEAK OF THE ENCOUNTER.

IN MY GODDAMN OBSESSIVE ZEAL, I EVEN RESORTED TO SUPERSTITIONS AND CHARMS.

OBSERVE: A FRAGMENT OF THE *TRUE* SKULL.

FOUND IN A PIT IN NEW YORK.

Feh.

TINK

AS THE SPHERE FADED AWAY, I WONDERED IF THE BLUE MAN WOULD EVER RECOVER FROM HIS FOLLY -- IF THE SOURCE OF HIS FEROCITY HAD BEEN GELDED.

ONE DAY, BRILLA SESSION, YOU SHALL WEAR MY CHAIN!

HE SPED AWAY, NEVER TO BE SEEN IN THIS AREA AGAIN.

I WONDER HOW DIFFERENT THE OUTCOME, IF ONLY HE HAD REMAINED A MOMENT LONGER...

...AN ABERRATION.

SOME MIGHT SAY A MIRACLE.

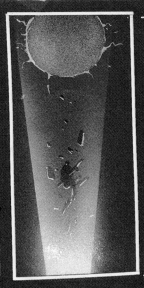

KLANG!

BUT I AM NO MAGICIAN OR PRIEST. I UNDERSTAND LITTLE OF SUCH THINGS.

...AM THE INDIGENOUS
...HIEF OF THESE
...ESOLATE ISLANDS.

AND AS THE PILE OF BLACK,
SMELLY METAL SLOWLY
SHOOK ITSELF ALIVE...

...I FINALLY REALIZED
THE BLUE MAN'S
SENSE OF DESPAIR.

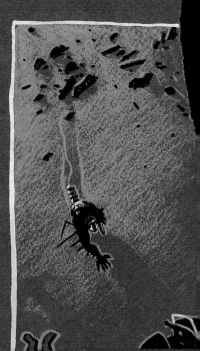

THIS WORLD CAN NEVER ESCAPE THE DEVIL'S INFLUENCE.

NOR HE ITS UNYIELDING GRASP.

THE EN